KEEPING PET
DUCKS

KEEPING PET
DUCKS

A comprehensive
guide to choosing
your breed, caring
for them and
enjoying their
company

LIZ WRIGHT

Interpet Publishing

Published by Interpet Publishing
Vincent Lane,
Dorking,
Surrey
RH4 3YX
England

Reprinted 2012

ISBN 978-1-8428-62193

Editor: Hilary Russell
Designer: Sue Casebourne Rose

Production Management:
Pepperbox Press Ltd.
Printed and bound in China

THE AUTHOR

Liz Wright has been editor of *Smallholder* magazine since 1987 and has been privileged to work with poultry experts from this country and abroad. She also pays tribute to the great poultry men and women from the past whose passion has been reflected in some of the beautiful breeds mentioned in this book. She lives on a smallholding with her partner, their poultry, which of course includes ducks, ponies and bees. Liz would like to dedicate this book to Valerie Charlesworth who was the owner of Smallholder for many years and who was always supportive of a then fledgling editor and always had confidence in Liz. Also, a special mention for Christopher Marler where Liz worked when she was a teenager and where she first encountered beautiful waterfowl sparking a life-time interest in ducks and geese.

Liz believes that the history of domestic ducks is also one of people and their relationship with the land; the revival of duck keeping reflects a renewed interest in these lovely birds which as well as laying eggs, if well kept, are a delightful family pet.

Liz is also an admirer of Peter Scott and is lucky to live near the Lincolnshire washes; one of her most favourite places and where she and her partner can enjoy watching the wild cousins of her domestic pals.

Contents

Introduction 6

What do ducks do? 8

Duck breeds 10

Ducks on show 20

How to buy ducks 22

Duck housing 24

Fencing out foxes 28

Ducks to water 30

Feeding ducks 32

Settling in your ducks 34

Ducks day by day 36

How to handle a duck 38

Duck eggs 40

Natural or artificial hatching? 44

Taking care of ducklings 50

What is good health? 52

Basic health care 54

Common ailments 56

Glossary 60

Index 63

✦ Introduction

▲ Free range ducks foraging during the day – but beware of predators.

I T'S EASIER TO KEEP pet ducks than many people think because there are such a wide variety of breeds, this means that there is a breed for almost every situation. Ducks do need water but not necessarily a huge pond or a flowing river – some breeds can manage very well with a small artificial pool, perhaps a hard plastic paddling pool. As long as they can get in and out of the pool (waddling on webs doesn't make you very athletic) and, most importantly, dip their whole head under the water to keep their bill and eyes clean, they are happy. You need to be able to easily clean out the pool as it will soon become very messy and that is where an artificial pool that can be easily emptied and moved when necessary becomes easier than a fixed pool.

Ducks also need suitable food in the form of

▲ Duck housing for their more athletic wild fowl counterparts.

a balanced ration supplied in a bag, a little corn and they do like to forage for invertebrates so they need a moveable run with plenty of space or to be let out to forage during the day. They need strong housing and good fencing to protect them from predators – foxes are particularly keen on ducks and if you don't see any foxes before you keep ducks, sadly you will see rather a lot once Charlie Fox hears them quacking. As with any livestock they need some daily care and most importantly, an owner who can notice any signs of ill health or discomfort (although when well kept they are very hardy), but they are not hard to keep when you know how!

Throughout the rest of this comprehensive book, we aim to give you a guide to choosing your breed, meeting their needs and enjoying their company – and for most breeds there is the added advantage of some tasty duck eggs!

✒ What do ducks do?

▲ Ducks love water but are happy with smaller ponds too.

DUCKS ARE DELIGHTFUL. Some earliest memories are made from feeding quacking, enthusiastic ducks at a local park or river. They are a pleasure to look at and become very friendly and endearing, making colourful and manageable pets. If you raise a duckling from young (which will involve some skilled management with additional heat supplied), it will often "imprint" and become attached to the person who reared it. But even if you get older birds, if they have been reared in a domestic situation, they should be reasonably placid and with plenty of time and

attention they will get to know you – perhaps even too much so as ours often stand quacking outside our back door!

But although charming to keep, domestic duck breeds were developed for commercial purposes with the egg trade very popular in the mid twentieth century. Some of our most famous and colourful breeds such as the exquisite Silver Appleyard and the striking Khaki Campbell (so named after the uniforms of the soldiers in the Boer War) were carefully bred to produce really stunning numbers of good sized eggs – 300 plus per year were recorded in the Campbells.

Ducks are also excellent gardeners (though they can't tell weeds from garden flowers!) Runner ducks in particular search out snails and slugs and if allowed into the vegetable plot before it is sown, can drastically reduce the number of garden pests.

Domestic Ducks and their Wildfowl Cousins

For pet ducks, and in domestic situations such as gardens, it is from the domestic duck breeds that

▲ Wildfowl do need water and are naturally more timid.

▲ All domestic ducks, except Muscovies, originate from genes of the wild Mallard.

you need to select your ducks. They all originate from the genes of the wild Mallard (and the markings in many breeds reflect this) apart from one, the Muscovy duck which originates from a perching tree duck. Wildfowl are such breeds as the spectacular Mandarin, the striking black and white Tufted duck, the Mallard (although domestic ducks originate from it, it is classified as a wild fowl), Teal and Wigeon. Although beautiful to look at they have a different set of needs to the domestic duck and normally need to be kept in large aviaries or on lakes. They can be perching ducks, diving ducks or dabbling ducks and you have to know which species you have to be able to provide the right environment. There are also breeds that don't mix well. Make sure you start with the domestic duck breeds and if wild fowl ducks appeal to you then you will have gained some initial duck experience.

There are also commercial breeds that are bred for the table but they do find their way into private homes – they are normally white in plumage and grow very quickly – from duckling to table weight in seven weeks – but they do make good pets and are very docile. Don't let them get too fat so provide plenty of room for exercise and they will live much longer as a result. They lay quite well.

CULTURAL DUCKS

Ducks
0 ducks are beautiful things!
But ducks are comical things:-
As comical as you.
Quack!
They waddle round, they do.
They eat all sorts of things.
And then they quack.
  FW Harvey

✳

A too trusting duck
Jemima Puddle-Duck, the famous heroine who nearly met a sticky end at the paws and teeth of the gentleman with sandy whiskers, is a very true

representation of the rather gentle natured, slow and not always the best of mothers farmyard duck. She is probably based on a duck of Aylesbury type but Beatrix Potter captures the nature of ducks very well!

✳

Ducks on film
Donald Duck from the Walt Disney studio is arguably the most famous duck in the movies and his popularity has lasted since his introduction in 1942. Disney studios have built up a whole raft of duck characters

since his inception. Daisy Duck was his girlfriend but there are many others. Donald is probably based on a Pekin duck in shape.

✳

Ducks in modern music
In 1976 a disco record called 'Disco Duck' was number one for a week on American Billboard while Lemon Jelly had a hit with 'Nice weather for Ducks' (complete with watery sounds) in 2002.

✳

✔ Duck breeds

DUCK BREEDS are classified into bantam (which includes miniature – small versions of the large breed), light breeds (where you will find the duck breeds that lay the highest number of eggs) and heavy breeds (developed primarily for meat but most now are popular exhibition birds for their colour and beauty). In addition there is the Muscovy which is a distinctive breed on its own.

▲ A Call duck is a noisy bird.

Bantam breeds

If you have a small area, even a modest sized back garden, then choose these diminutive birds that are happy with an artificial pool and a more limited area – though they still need space to move and to forage.

The Call

The name says it all – these are noisy birds that just open their beaks and let fly with an amazingly large sound. Perhaps no near neighbours might be the prerequisite for keeping these! But they are a truly enchanting little duck, weighing in at around, or just over, 0.5 kg and looking like the old fashioned bath duck with their large head, large appealing eyes and cute but noisy little beaks. They come in a terrific range of colours from pure white through silver, mallard and pied with colours such as Butterscotch also on offer.

They originated from Holland and reached the UK before the 1850s and the USA shortly after. They are an ideal pet as they have an enthusiastic personality and are very alert – making them very good guard ducks! They can fly well so will need to have their wings clipped. They bond closely as families so always keep an established pair or trio together.

▲ This bantam is a Miniature Appleyard.

▲ A judge studying a Call duck.

HANDY HINTS

The Call duck is particularly small and therefore more at risk from predators (including winged predators) than other ducks. Ensure they have adequate protection especially when you are not at home.

❋

The Silver Appleyard miniature does love to go broody so if you don't want to breed, remove the eggs at least every day to try and stop them from sitting.

❋

Don't confuse the Silver Appleyard miniature with the Silver Bantam. They are separate breeds and the Silver Bantam duck has a lighter body with a distinct fawn head while her consort's breast and shoulders are red/brown laced with white.

bright blue flash on their wings. As with its large counterpart, this is a good layer but it is outstanding as a show bird and really stands out on the bench. They love to forage and are very busy birds.

They are especially good as children's pets and can become very tame. Because of their attractive nature there are excellent clubs and societies for enthusiasts of these ducks and so lots of advice and information is available.

The Silver Appleyard Miniature

This is a particularly ornamental bird that was developed in the 1980s and is a small version of the famous Silver Appleyard. They are truly striking with their contrasting silver plumage against the fawn and brown of the top feathers and the

▲ This is a showy Silver Miniature Appleyard.

Light duck breeds

This category of ducks contains some of the highest egg layers. Breeders in the early to mid twentieth century were very keen on developing high egg laying strains of hardy ducks.

▶ The Khaki Campbell also comes in pure white.

The Khaki Campbell

This is perhaps the most famous of the light breeds, so named for the Khaki worn by the soldiers going to the Boer War in 1901. It is a handsome semi-upright breed that has a green hooded drake with a khaki coloured body. The duck is khaki all over. They combine a very high capacity for egg laying – up to 300 a year in some strains – with the ability to actively search for insects and food – of course they still need a good basic ration provided for them as well. They have a docile nature and they don't fly, making them an ideal domestic duck. The Khaki is the high egg layer but this duck has also been developed in pure white.

The Magpie

This is a rarer bird as it is quite hard to breed a well marked example – as its name suggests it is black and white but the markings should be such that when you view the duck with closed wings, there is a heart shape over the back. There should also be a black cap. This is difficult to achieve and breeders spend many years breeding good examples. The duck is also a good layer of around 200 eggs a year (which may be bluey green as well as white) and it does make a good pet. It is very alert and perhaps a bit less placid than the other breeds mentioned. It cannot fly well, if at all.

◀ The Magpie is a very alert duck.

The Welsh Harlequin

This breed was developed even later, in the 1940s, and had a chequered history, all but disappearing in the 1960s. It is popular again now and is an ideal domestic duck being very hardy but calm and liking to forage close to home. It doesn't fly. It is an average layer at 100 – 150 eggs a year but the breed was developed to be dual purpose, which means for eggs and for the table. These days they tend to be kept for their attractive plumage and egg laying capacities. The drake has plumage similar to a mallard with a white ring round the neck while the duck is honey fawn in colour.

▲ The Welsh Harlequin is hardy and calm.

The Abacot Ranger

This breed was developed slightly later in the 1920s and again with the aim of producing a high egg layer. This duck can lay up to 250 eggs a year and is also semi-erect, a good forager, rarely flies and has a placid nature. Unlike the Campbell it is a good mother and sitter. Both sexes are hooded, the drake with a strong green sheen on its dark brown head and the duck with a darker brown head. The bill of the drake is yellowish green while the female is dark grey, meaning you can tell their sex at a comparatively early age.

◄ The Abacot Ranger is a good layer.

The Indian Runner

This is categorised as a light breed but it is certainly a unique duck breed for, as its name implies, it is exceptionally upright in stance; so much so that in the Standards for the breed its body is described as being inclined from the vertical at between 50% – 80%. The length is also measured when in a straight line and is from 24 to 32 inches (60 – 80cms) depending on sex. This makes it a long duck, partly because of its long body and partly because of its long, elegant neck. The legs though are short and strong as they have to be to support the angle of the body and are set slightly back to compensate, but they can move very fast indeed – they are not called "Runners" for no reason. The duck is thought to originate from the East Indies and possibly Malaya; there are reports of classes in poultry shows for Runner ducks from as early as 1876 in Britain. They were also known in Australia and New Zealand by the early 1900s and world-wide shortly afterwards due to their tough ability to travel on trade boats. Although

▲ Runner ducks have been competing in shows since 1876.

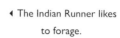

there are reports of early Runners flying, they no longer fly but they do move quickly on their strong legs and can be quite flighty so it is best to get to know them well before you let them free range. They love to forage and range and are the perfect duck for hunting down snails and slugs and are even commercially used in some gardens and

◀ The Indian Runner likes to forage.

vineyards for just this purpose. It is a stunning looking duck in a number of established colours including white, fawn, trout (similar to mallard colouring), black, blue and chocolate but breeders are constantly coming up with new colours.

It is also incredibly useful as it competes with the Campbell for high egg laying performance with old records giving up to 300 eggs per duck a year. Now about 180 – 200 is more likely which is still very respectable. You can keep drakes together without females and they don't fight but they are very over attentive to females so you must only keep one drake to a number of ducks to avoid injury to the females. Because they are light they do less damage to the ground than other ducks. They will swim but they prefer foraging so as long as you have a small pond where they can dip heads and necks and splash, they are happy.

HANDY HINTS

You will often see this breed at County Shows in sheepdog and duck displays as they herd well.

❊

This duck is often known as the gardener's friend but it cannot tell weeds from crops so keep it away from the vegetable plot in spring!

Heavy duck breeds

While the light breeds contain the higher egg layers, some people argue that within the heavy breeds are some of the most beautiful examples of ducks. Originally developed for the table, now many of these breeds are kept because their striking plumage makes them ideal for competing at poultry shows. These ducks do appreciate a good sized artificial pond, especially for breeding.

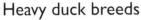

◀ The Aylesbury duck has blue eyes and a pale bill.

▼ The Aylesbury is a weighty duck..

The Aylesbury

Few white ducks that are called Aylesbury really are this famous breed. The clue is that a pure bred Aylesbury will have blue eyes and a distinctive flesh coloured or pinky white bill, not orange. The legs are orange. If the bill is orange it is likely to be a cross bred Pekin and therefore a commercial meat bird. It is a huge size and the drake weights up to 12½ lb (5.6 kg). It is placid and loves to eat so be sure to provide some space for exercise or it will get over fat – especially important for pet ducks. It lays between 25 – 100 or so eggs a year.

▲ A prize-winning Rouen male.

▲ The Rouen duck combines an impressive body with good egg laying.

The Rouen

This calm, stately bird originates from France and, by its admirers, is thought to be the most impressive of the large breeds with its Mallard type colouring on a vast, box shaped body carried on strong, short legs. It needs space to walk for foraging as it will otherwise quickly get too fat if it doesn't move about. It is a slow maturer of up to 20 weeks to get adult plumage and will lay a respectable 100 plus eggs per year.

The Pekin

This is the upright white duck of the heavy breeds and is sometimes known as the Penguin duck as a result. Although the breed dates back to ancient times in China, its arrival in the USA and Britain in the late 1800s was welcomed with excitement and the breed soon formed the backbone of the commercial hybrid table duck. It is a delightful duck, placid and friendly. It cannot fly and loves to waddle in a decent sized range looking for invertebrates. Not a bad egg layer, they can achieve around 100 or so eggs a year. They have very open, almost fluffy feathering so do not do well in muddy conditions and need plenty of water to keep clean. This open feathering also attracts parasites and even fly eggs. They can make good broodies and rear their own ducklings.

▲ The Pekin is sometimes known as the Penguin duck.

Silver Appleyard

Another striking heavy breed that was bred for utility (meat and egg) production but now is also valued for the compact, colourful body with its silver points and, in the case of the drake, claret breast. It loves to forage, gains weight very quickly so needs to be able to exercise and is a good egg layer at up to 180 eggs per year.

▲ The Silver Appleyard loves to forage.

▲ The Muscovy duck is descended from a tree duck and flies well.

The Muscovy

The Muscovy duck is classified as a heavy duck but is the only domestic duck not descended from the Mallard, having a tree duck as its ancestor. This makes it different in looks and personality from other ducks and it seems duck keepers are split into admirers and those that don't like them. They are low to the ground and a drake weighs up to 14lbs but they are impressive fliers with personality, which you either like or find annoying. They do need water for floating or splashing but they really enjoy foraging, even taking in small mammals as part of their varied diet. Don't keep them shut up in a small run but do clip their wings to stop them flying (although many will return home in the evening of their own accord!). They are superb and fierce mothers, raising prodigious sized broods with an egg incubation period of 35 days, not the normal 28 days for domestic ducks. Perhaps not a beginner's duck but a truly characterful one and this writer is right in the admirers camp for their distinctive and determined attitude to life.

▲ The Muscovy duck is a bird with character.

✦ Ducks on show

UCK KEEPERS have been keen on showing their birds since the late Victorian age but it is a hobby that is proving very popular today as well. Poultry shows which include classifications for domestic waterfowl are held most weekends throughout the year and also form part of agricultural shows. The entry fees are usually quite modest and the only requirement of entry is that you have a true example of the breed class that you enter and that you present a healthy duck in a clean state for judging. Cages are provided and exhibitors have to leave while judging takes place. A duck that wins its class goes on to compete in its section and might even go on to compete for the coveted title of Best Waterfowl in Show or the much prized, Best in Show. There are some shows that are purely for waterfowl.

The best way to get started is to contact the Poultry Club of Great Britain and get a list of shows for the year. Then pick one that features the breeds that interest you and go along and see the ducks. Their owners are normally more than happy to point out their finer points and to talk duck keeping and of course you get to see really good examples of every breed. This is helpful not only for people who want to show ducks but great for people thinking of keeping them as they can see real life examples of the breeds and hear what duck keepers have to say about them.

If you then want to have a go at showing, take a long, hard, critical look at your ducks and decide which ones are the best examples of their breed. Then you will need to get them as tame as you can so that they are not too frightened at the show and show themselves off to their best advantage. You may need to separate them from the flock for some "pen-taming" prior to the show. Before the show you will need to wash the ducks, making sure that the light parts are spotlessly clean and that the legs and feet (webs) do not show any dirt. A light oiling with Vaseline is sometimes done to show them off. Watch what others are doing at the show and ask questions – most people are happy to share information. Junior Exhibitors have their own classes which may involve taking the bird out of the pen and showing how well they can handle them plus answering a few questions on the breed.

When the judging is done, come back and see where you were placed. If you won, do ask for a criticism of the duck so you know what you did right and if you didn't win, it is even more important to find out why and try to improve. Above all have fun with like minded people and beautiful birds.

▲ You can learn a lot by volunteering as a steward.

B.W.A. Show Trophies

▲ Top prizes for top ducks.

▶ It's a great hobby for young people.

▲ A show duck needs to be used to being handled.

HANDY HINTS

Most duck shows have pre-entries so you need to get a schedule some weeks ahead of the show date and enter.

✳

Make sure you have good transport with a strong, well ventilated container.

✳

Take your own duck food and clip-on cage water containers in case none are provided.

▲ Pens are provided for the ducks.

How to buy ducks

SO YOU HAVE BEEN to a show and chosen the breed, you have identified suitable housing, learnt about management and decided how to provide water. Ducks are definitely for you but how do you buy them?

The best way to buy ducks is direct from the breeder who will be able to tell you their history, show you their parents and offer you help and advice in your early duck keeping career. You can find a breeder by getting in touch with the Club for that breed – nearly all duck breeds have either their own club or are part of a larger waterfowl club. They will have a list of breeders in your area though it is arguably more important to buy the best birds you can rather than just the closest so be prepared to travel. If you are considering breeding then you must buy good quality stock. Otherwise you can look in specialist smallholding and poultry magazines for advertisements, your local newspaper or go on-line. It is best not to buy unseen if possible and a good idea to see the premises where they are kept. You can also buy from auction sales or private sales where you buy what is in the pen for either a pre-agreed fee or in an auction. If you are going to use this method, be sure you know what you are looking for in terms of breed standard and be able to check birds for

▲ Buy your duck direct from the breeder.

▲ A chance to look before you buy.

good health and age. Try and get the name and contact details of the seller so you can get in touch if you have queries after the sale.

Most people want to buy young ducks that are sexed and these tend to be from 10 – 20 weeks old. The advantage is that they have their life ahead of them and are still young enough to tame and get into your ways. But don't rule out older ducks – ducks live to be a reasonable age – mine were over ten years old when they died. An established breeding trio could teach you something. Buying ducklings is not for the beginner as normally they cannot be sexed, so you could be buying all drakes, and they will need specialist care and heat. If you do buy them, make sure you know exactly how to rear them and be prepared to sort out the male to female ratio. It is actively cruel to keep more than one drake with a small group of ducks as drakes will harass the females physically, to the point of injury, during breeding season and competing drakes will continually try and prove their libido. Most drakes can be kept without females and vice versa.

✔ Duck housing

IME SPENT IN PREPARATION for ducks is never wasted. Take a look at where you intend to keep them – will there be any problems with near neighbours through noise or smell? Will the house be sited so that it remains cool even in hot weather but safe from winter winds and rain? Realistically, is there sufficient ground not to be paddled into a muddy swamp? Ducks really are very messy with their large webbed feet and they also do manage to produce quite large amounts of sloppy duck droppings which need to be cleared up (and usually composted in a controlled way). The area where you are keeping them needs to be easily cleaned. Waste food attracts vermin, usually in the form of rats, so the duck housing needs to be kept clean and free of old food. The pond needs to be sited where it can be cleaned out and emptied. Clearly identify a well drained site, away from close neighbours and not too close to shrubs or woodland that would attract foxes.

The next step is to provide housing, fencing and water.

Duck housing needs to be very secure so that foxes cannot break into the house at night.

The ducks will need to be shut up at dusk and not let out until the morning. Unlike hens, ducks like to go through a door all together so you need a door that will accommodate this.

You can buy purpose built duck housing, these are normally low, stoutly build sheds with good sized doors or you can buy a garden shed and adapt it for housing. The other option, if you already have a secure building is to use that – especially good if you have an airy, brick built building going spare. Ducks are very simple in that they only require to be kept draught free and dry. They do need good ventilation so a high roof does help and draught free windows – normally open spaces covered with wire not glass placed higher up the shed – must be provided. Ducks suffer in poor, stuffy ventilation and will become ill.

Unlike hens, ducks do not readily

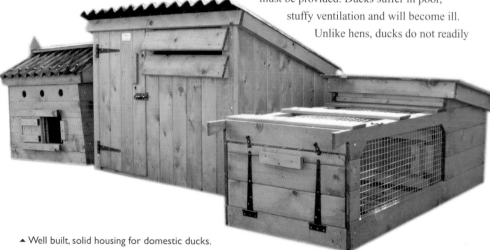

▲ Well built, solid housing for domestic ducks.

◀ Ornamental duck housing for wild fowl.

▼ A house needs to be fox proof and be well ventilated.

use a nest box and are quite casual about where they lay eggs unless they are thinking about going broody. But placing a piece of wood, about two inches or so high, in a dark part of the house might convince them that this is a good nesting place so it's worth a try. Normally they will choose where they want to lay and it is up to you to keep the area clean and freshly bedded. Ducks do well on straw and shavings too can be used. Remember their webs are very sensitive to damage so you don't want a sharp area round the house – don't use gravel for example. Smooth paving slabs will give some hard standing.

▲ Select the size of house suitable for the size and number of ducks.

Other forms of duck housing are small moveable arks, more usually used in conjunction with larger natural ponds. The clue is in the word moveable – they should be moved around so that the area round the house doesn't become muddy but if they are not connected to a run then you won't be able to move them too far at a time or the ducks won't know where to go back to.

Although avian flu has not been a problem in recent years, do remember that in the event of an outbreak you might need to keep ducks confined inside for several weeks, so if you have a choice of using a bigger house or can

▲ Choose the housing suitable for your breed of duck.

▲ Duck housing within the centre of a lake – be careful if it freezes as foxes can cross ice.

use a run that can be bird proofed, it might be a good idea to put that in place early rather than when or if avian flu reaches our shores again. It is helpful too if the house is large and airy enough to confine birds for short periods and/or has a safe run.

▲ Housing for wild fowl depends on their natural habit such as perching, diving or dabbling.

🐦 Fencing out foxes

DUCKS SEEM TO BE EVEN more attractive to Mr. Fox than chickens. Most of them have limited flight too so it makes them easy pickings. In some areas, ducks will be able to range freely during the day but for others the fox problem is so great that you will need a fox proof fence. The domestic dog is also a problem for ducks – be sure to keep your own pet under control, a duck cannot tell the difference between a dog "playing" with it in a friendly way or a duck killer. If you go out to work all day you will almost certainly need to provide a fox and duck proof enclosure for your feathered friends.

Fencing is possibly the biggest expense in terms of money and practical outlay but it is also the most important if your duck keeping is going to be successful for you and your ducks. To really fence out a fox you need to provide a 2m high fence with an overhang so that the predator cannot climb over it and it may also need to be sunk into the ground so that it cannot be dug under either. Alternatively a strip of electric fence just above, but not touching, the ground will deter digging. The fencing needs properly straining. Another alternative is poultry netting. Ducks do tend to take time to realise that this is electrified and there is the danger of them getting their necks stuck through it and getting repeated shocks. Take time when you first use it to ensure they understand that it is going to give them a shock – watch them carefully and turn it on for the first time when you are there to take action if necessary. To work effectively against predators it must be working well all the time so it will need testing with a fence tester from time to time and either run from a self charging solar battery or have a plentiful supply of new batteries. Electric fences sited where people might touch them need to carry a warning notice. Ducks don't usually leave fixed boundaries such as hedges or solid or wire mesh fencing of up to a metre high so it may be that you have a good sized (and fully fenced against predators) run for when you are not around and you let them out to range more fully when you are outside with them or quite obviously at home. Some areas suffer from predators more than others – foxes don't normally strike during the day unless they are

▲ Fencing is expensive but essential.

▲ Foxes strike at night so make sure your ducks are safely penned up.

used to human contact or particularly hungry because they have cubs (early summer). Another thing to watch out for is adjacent scrub, woodland or plantation where foxes can have cover.

Don't be outfoxed – you may not have seen a fox before you had ducks but it is almost certain that there will be one close by and will show itself when you do start duck keeping. Be prepared.

🐦 Ducks to water

ALL DUCKS WILL NEED some form of water as they are waterfowl – they are adapted to need water. Wildfowl will need deep water and access to good sized ponds but domestic ducks can usually manage very well with an easily cleanable artificial pool, although many of the heavy duck breeds do need more room. Duck pools can be bought and are simple, heavy plastic bowl-type designs but you can use hard plastic paddling pools or any suitable container that is about a metre wide and about 30cms high. Ducks do quickly foul water

so you need to be able to empty it and refill at regular intervals. Unlike chickens, ducks are not athletic birds – they waddle rather than walk – so you will need to build a ramp up to and out of the water. They cannot just get out of a steep sided pool, even when comparatively low. You can put in a permanent structure but a more moveable design of stout wood resting on bricks that gradually slopes up into the pool and an underwater breeze block or bricks so the duck has something to stand on to get out, will usually do the job well. In addition to the

▲ Even a small paddling pool will do the job.

swimming/splashing water, you need a deeper tub or bucket where the duck can totally immerse the head and neck. If they cannot do this, they cannot keep their eyes and nostrils clean and this will lead to serious diseases. The splashing water will help them to activate their preen gland which is situated near the tail and releases oil when the duck is splashing. This enables the duck to keep the plumage in good

condition so it is essential that there is sufficient water for them to do this. A moveable pond can be located in different areas so none become waterlogged.

A permanent pond still needs to be able to be cleaned so it is preferable to construct one from shallow concrete (pond liners tend to get shredded by the strong claws that some duck breeds possess though they may work with the less energetic breeds). It is a good idea to build a drain into them for emptying or at least some way they can be swept or washed out as they will need cleaning. A hard surface round the edge will help to stop the mud but don't use gravel as it will injure the ducks' feet.

If you already have an established pond, be careful not to have too many ducks as the water will become polluted and may not support any other form of life. A free flowing stream is ideal but of course, the ducks may float away on it and also watch out for water based predators like mink.

◀ Ducks must be able to climb out of the pool.

🦆 Feeding ducks

▲ Ensure there are sufficient feeders so shy ducks don't miss out.

A S WITH ANY LIVESTOCK, ducks require a balanced diet. Even when they are free range and are foraging for invertebrates and other tasty morsels, they still need a nutritionally correct ration and this is best provided in the form of a bagged duck food. Most pet ducks will simply need a basic duck pellet for maintenance and this will contain all the necessary proteins, carbohydrates, minerals and vitamins. Other rations available include Duckling starter crumbs (if you can't get duck then you will have to use chick crumbs but ask for those without a coccidiostat). These will take them up to around four to five weeks when they move on to Grower pellets. They can then either have a general maintenance ration or they can have Breeder pellets if reproducing or Layer pellets for high egg laying ducks. Finally there are Finishing pellets for those ducks heading for the table and Ornamental Waterfowl pellets for wildfowl. Ducks can live on chicken rations but choose those with the least amount of additives as they are not always good for ducks – go for a free range pellet or even an organic one.

All ducks must have plenty of water available next to their feed – you will see them introduce water to their feed and it all gets rather messy. Feeding a dry pellet to a duck without water will upset the digestion, especially if they are then forced to look for water after they have eaten. Ducks also love grain feeds in the form of whole wheat or cracked maize in winter when it helps to combat the cold. Again they need water to feed – you can put the wheat in shallow trays actually in water. Bread is a controversial subject – it is not really very good for ducks but if fed as a treat in small quantities and

▲ Wheat can be fed in shallow trays.

▲ There is a wide range of feeders and drinkers for every situation.

soaked in water first, it shouldn't do any harm. Ducks also like cold, boiled potatoes and they love lettuce.

You will need to provide grit as well, not oyster shell which is different. The grit helps them to grind their food. If they are on free range they will probably find their own but it is best to have some handy anyway and if they are confined they must have grit available at all times.

A duck can eat about 150g a day (5 oz) but that's just a rough guide. Your eyes are your best gauge of how much to feed. You don't want lots of waste food left over that will attract rats and other vermin but you also don't want hungry ducks so observe how quickly they finish their food and feed accordingly. You will need more food in cold weather and winter when there isn't much for them to find on range.

Settling in your ducks

BRINGING DUCKS HOME for the first time is a great experience if you are fully prepared for them. They will naturally be worried – it is a new place and they don't know what is happening, so make sure that everything is ready for them and you can just put them into their house and run and quietly leave them to it. You will need to keep them confined for at least a few days so you will need a run, or if you are putting them into an existing building, you will need to have the moveable pond in there with them. Ducks do not do well in close confinement so make sure

▲ Ducks soon learn that your visit means food!

you have given them enough space – six ducks will need at least three square metres – and that's only for a few days or so.

Ask the seller what they have been eating and even if it is not a good ration, don't change them too quickly to their new balanced ration – gradually change over until you are feeding them correctly. Don't expect them to be friendly to begin with – they will soon realise that you are a friend when you turn up every day with their feed. If you want to get to know them, get a chair and sit quietly with them while they get accustomed to their new surroundings. Keep noisy children (and adults!) away from them and don't let even friendly dogs near them – ducks don't know that a dog is not going to harm them. If they need to have their wings clipped – do so before you let them into their new pen.

Watch them carefully for a few days and when you think they have settled down you can let them out to forage – this might take longer for more timid ducks.

▲ Ducks need to get acclimatized
to their new home.

HOW TO CLIP WINGS

This is a painless procedure not to be confused with pinioning, and is the clipping of the flight feathers on one wing – the primary and secondary feathers. This will unbalance the bird and prevent it from flying. They re-grow with every moult so will need doing regularly.

Pinioning is not normally done on domestic breeds but is for wild fowl and is done when they are very young ducklings. This is the permanent removal of part of the wing so they will never be able to fly.

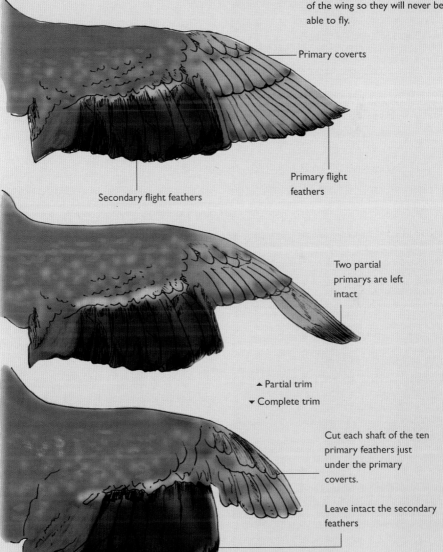

Primary coverts

Primary flight feathers

Secondary flight feathers

Two partial primarys are left intact

▲ Partial trim
▼ Complete trim

Cut each shaft of the ten primary feathers just under the primary coverts.

Leave intact the secondary feathers

🕊 Ducks day by day

▲ Check for lameness in the morning.

▲ Watching your ducks is a pleasure.

Your ducks will soon become part of your everyday life. In the morning they will have to be let out of their house into their large run or to forage. They can have their first feed of the day and this is when you will check to see that they are all well. If a duck does not come out of the house then it will either be laying, going broody or it is not well. If laying it will be crouched in laying position with legs tucked under her but if ill it will be hunched at the back of the house looking miserable. Also check for lameness. Collect any eggs – they normally lay in the few hours after dawn – and make sure they have plenty of clean, fresh water. Take time to talk to them and enjoy watching them.

At dusk they will have to be shut in again, they are normally very sensible and go into their house so you just have to shut the door. Make sure you see them a few hours before dusk as well to check they are eating up and maybe give them a feed of wheat or maize. As you shut them up check there is no waste food to attract unwanted rats. There is no need to put food or water in the house at night as they won't feed or drink in the hours of darkness but you have a responsibility to make sure they are let out promptly each day as well as kept safe at night.

As well as being pleasurable, watching the birds is useful. You can tell if there is any bullying going on, whether they look clean – if they look dirty they could be ill, the drakes could be making the ducks' life miserable by too many attentions or there is not enough clean water on offer. You will also get to know

▲ At dusk your ducks will be shut in again.

them individually – the ones that come out first, the confident, the shy, the tame and the nervous. If you know how they behave normally then it is easy to tell if there are any problems and catch them before they harm the birds.

HANDY HINTS

Watch the weather forecast – provide shelter in bad weather and shade in hot weather.

❊

Have a check for eggs at dusk as well in case a duck is laying later than normal.

❊

Why not take a hand titbit to encourage them to get to know you?

❊

▲ Watch for signs of bullying in mixed flocks.

✦ How to handle a duck

▲ It is vital to know how to catch your duck safely, especially if it escapes at a show!

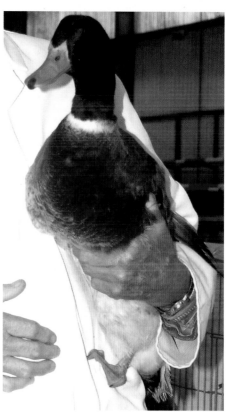

U NLIKE CATS AND DOGS, ducks are not normally soothed by handling unless they are very tame. Therefore any contact needs to be calm, skilled and efficient. To catch a duck, first think carefully about how to achieve it – chasing and cornering is not humane and will terrify them. It is best to catch the duck at dusk when it is going to roost for the night as it will be easy to quietly remove it from its sleeping place. If you have to catch a sick duck or move a bully, then plan where you are going to confine it and quietly herd it towards the enclosure – mustering enough help to make this effective. You can use boards or hurdles as a funnel to guide the duck to the enclosure.

Once in the pen, keep calm and wait a few minutes for them to quieten down. Then quietly but firmly reach for the duck aiming to get control of the wings – wildly flapping wings will soon get injured and can be quite

▲ A waterfowl workshop is a good place to learn handling techniques.

painful for the handler too. Grasp them firmly but gently and keep them still. It helps to have another person to block off the duck's escape route – it is really not good to chase them around. If you cannot catch the duck after a couple of attempts, stop and re-plan your approach – maybe you need more people or you need to confine the duck in a smaller space by using boards.

To hold the duck, bring the duck towards your body keeping the wings under control. Your hand goes under the body to keep the legs still with your fingers between the legs. Never pull them tightly together as that is likely to cause internal injury especially in high egg layers. The bird will be resting on your hand with the other hand still restraining its wings. You can put the head under your arm if the bird is very lively.

To travel the bird use a well ventilated and safe container – the bird should be able to stand but not have so much room that they don't have any support from the sides. They must be kept cool in transit and be able to breathe clean air. A pet carrier of appropriate size is a good choice. Drive carefully and don't be jerky – the boxes should not slide about in the vehicle.

✔ Duck eggs

▲ Duck eggs are richer than hen's eggs and especially good for baking.

DUCK EGGS ARE DELICIOUS and are usually rather larger than a hen's egg – depending on the breed of duck. As with any egg they are very nutritious and now that experts believe that they are no longer associated with causing raised cholesterol levels, you can enjoy them even more. They contain about 100 calories each, again depending on size, and are mainly water with about 10 – 15 % protein and fat – all dependent on size and breed. Duck eggs are richer than hens' eggs making them really good for baking cakes. They can be eaten in the same way as hens' eggs but it is advisable to thoroughly cook them to be completely food safe, especially for pregnant women, older people and vulnerable groups.

They have a creamy texture and one duck's

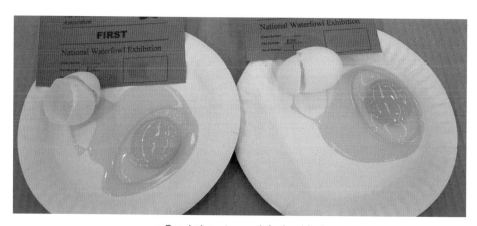

▲ One duck egg is enough for breakfast!

▲ Ducks can be the birds that lay golden eggs for their taste and quantity.

egg is usually enough for breakfast because of their larger size.

To store eggs, store them point down, in a cool (but not frozen) place, away from strong smelling foods. The same applies if you are storing them to "set" (put under broody hens or ducks). Make sure you devise a way of storing them in date order – if you have a couple of ducks that lay 200 eggs a year, you will soon get quite swamped by eggs and you need to use the oldest first.

Longer term storage of eggs is best done by boiling and pickling but the old fashioned method was to store them in soluble sodium silicate (waterglass). If you choose this method be sure you don't put in any with cracked shells. You can freeze eggs without their shells to use in baking recipes and you can always freeze the egg whites for meringue – perhaps if you have used the yolks in a recipe. Otherwise sell your surplus to friends and family – check the regulations but unless you are selling at a stall away from home it is normally legal to make informal sales of un-graded eggs in a small way.

You don't need a drake to produce eggs – ducks will lay anyway but the eggs of course will not be fertile.

◀ You don't have to have a drake, like this splendid Miniature Crested, to ensure an egg supply from your ducks.

🦆 So what is an egg?

A N EGG CONSISTS OF five parts, the yolk, the egg white (albumen) and shell – all of which can be seen easily – plus there is also a germinal disc inside the yolk and the shell membrane. All eggs also have an air pocket which is very small when fresh but increases towards hatching. The egg is a marvellous thing in that it contains all the nutrients that the chick inside will need during the incubation period of 28 days (35 in Muscovy ducks) and also for the day after hatching (the chick will have absorbed these). Because of the pores on the outside, water vapour, oxygen and carbon dioxide are able to function. The chick is a single fertilised cell – the germinal disc – that sits on the surface of the yolk. As it grows it uses up the yolk, some of the albumen and some calcium from the egg shell interior. The air pocket develops from a small pocket to the optimum size for survival as the embryo grows. If the atmosphere around the egg is too humid (contains too much moisture) then the egg cannot lose moisture and so the air pocket will be too small and if the atmosphere is too dry then it cannot absorb air so it is too large. In both cases the embryo cannot develop and will die. Luckily a broody duck or hen is naturally able to provide the

HANDY HINTS

When collecting eggs for either eating or hatching, carefully check the egg.
All cracked eggs for either purpose should be discarded – they won't hatch and the crack may have allowed harmful bacteria into the egg.

❄

Dirty eggs that need cleaning – ideally for hatching collect clean eggs. Wash eggs before storing for home use – if really dirty then discard.

For hatching don't use over large or over small eggs. Double yolkers won't hatch. Also don't hatch oddly shaped eggs such as too round or long and thin – they cannot develop normally. Thin shelled eggs should also be put aside – they might break under the duck or in the incubator causing the rest of the hatch to go bad. Rough shelled eggs where the pores cannot function cannot hatch.

❄

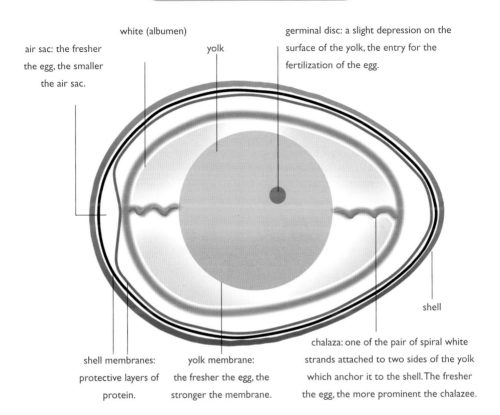

air sac: the fresher the egg, the smaller the air sac.

white (albumen)

yolk

germinal disc: a slight depression on the surface of the yolk, the entry for the fertilization of the egg.

shell

shell membranes: protective layers of protein.

yolk membrane: the fresher the egg, the stronger the membrane.

chalaza: one of the pair of spiral white strands attached to two sides of the yolk which anchor it to the shell. The fresher the egg, the more prominent the chalazee.

correct conditions for optimum hatching; artificial incubation involves trying to replicate these and sometimes it can be hard to get it right, although modern incubators are now very well designed.

A duck will lay a "clutch" of eggs – when she is going broody she will lay an egg a day into a nest she has made and when she has what she considers enough (5 –10), she will "sit" – that is go broody and sit on the eggs and incubate them. This way, although the eggs are laid on separate days,

they will all hatch at a similar time. When incubating, eggs are collected daily until there is sufficient for the incubator. They are kept in a cool but not cold (and certainly not the fridge) place until this point and it is best not to use eggs older than a week to a maximum of ten days old.

◆ Natural or artificial hatching?

SOME BREEDS ARE NOT GOOD mothers and the choice is made for you, if you want ducklings you will need to use an incubator. Some ducks are not great either and you get to know this as you try to breed. The great advantage of the incubator is that you can control when and where you hatch and you don't have the problem of the duck suddenly getting off the eggs and them going cold and therefore they stop developing. You know exactly when they are going to hatch and you can also handle the ducklings at an early age which keeps them much tamer. You can also hatch larger numbers of ducklings as you can put in more eggs than a duck can naturally sit on.

The great advantage of a natural mother duck is that you don't have to do much else other than keep her safe and provide food; she will do it all and the hatch rate – number of eggs incubated to ducklings hatched – is normally very high. There is also the pleasure of watching her with the ducklings which is a truly delightful experience.

The other alternative is to use a broody hen. Again, some breeds of hen are much broodier than others and the delightful Silkies and their crosses, absolutely love to go broody and adore

▲ A Gleevum Superior wooden incubator. This is a museum piece now, replaced by the modern electric incubators.

raising chicks. They are perfectly happy to sit on duck eggs and are very successful in hatching and raising them. The challenge is to have a broody hen available for hatching but sometimes you can borrow from a friend or neighbour. Of course the hen gets quite puzzled as her charges grow much bigger than her and head towards the water, leaving her clucking anxiously round the edge!

Dealing with a broody duck (or hen)

You can tell a broody bird as she will sit tight on her nest which will normally be lined with some of her feathers. The bird will be very defensive – if you try and move her she will become quite aggressive and peck at you and get very vocal in a way you will not have heard before. If you do manage to move her she will straight away try and go back to the nest and settle herself down.

The most important thing is to keep her safe. If she is broody outside where she is vulnerable to predators you have two choices – to try and move her which is not always successful or to build some kind of protection where she sits. If you move her, do so at

▲ A broody hen will hatch duck eggs.

night and keep her shut in the space so she gets used to it and doesn't try to get back to her chosen place. You will also need to provide food and water – she will get off the eggs for a short time to eat and drink but not for long, so it needs to be close at hand. Although she will need water to dip her head in, as she comes close to hatching replace it with a shallow container that the ducklings cannot drown in (yes, very young ducklings can drown if they get stuck in water and can't get out). Remember that as well as the fox who will take the duck, magpies, crows and rats will all enjoy the eggs so she will need

protection from all of these. (Some of these will take small ducklings too.)

She will/should sit for the whole 28 days and then take care of the hatchlings. If she gets off them with no intention of returning, then it could be that she has a problem with external parasites making it uncomfortable to sit – it is a good idea to treat all broody ducks for mite – get advice from your vet. But there are some ducks that are just bad sitters and although you can forgive her one or even two incomplete hatches, after that, note her down as not suitable for breeding and use an incubator.

Choosing and using an incubator

Quite simply the most important thing in using any kind of incubator is to carefully read the manual. Every manufacturer has designed their machine for a purpose and has tested it to get the best from it. The manual is an essential guide to that machine. If it doesn't have one, go on-line to find the manufacturer's contact details and get a replacement or speak to an incubator expert who has previously used the machine.

The incubators come as still air (warm air surrounds the eggs) or forced air or fan assisted (the warm air is directed evenly around the eggs. They also come as manual, semi-automatic or fully automatic. A duck will turn her eggs several times a day to ensure they develop evenly and to prevent the embryo sticking to the inner shell. In the absence of a duck, the eggs still need to be turned. For a manual, the operator physically turns them at least three times a day, in a semi-automatic you still have to do this but you can do it without opening the incubator by using a handle on the outside, or the fully automatic where the incubator has a small motor that turns them

▲ Speak to an expert before you choose an incubator.

▲ Small incubators.

▲ A small modern incubator will hatch duck eggs efficiently.

▲ Wild fowl lay different looking eggs which can be recognised from their breeds.

itself. The fan assisted, fully-automatic machine has become the most popular choice but an advantage of the semi-automatic is that it can involve the family in the hatching process, by actively taking responsibility to turn the eggs. Whichever method is used, stop turning the eggs three days before hatching. The usual temperature for the incubator is around 37.5°C. It must be sited where there are no extremes of temperature so not by an open window. Run it to temperature before putting in the eggs. Follow manufacturer's instructions for adding water but also take account of the humidity of the outer air.

Candle at 5–7 days to see if the air sac is forming – that means shining a bright light through the egg with a torch or a special egg candler.

HANDY HINTS

Keep a record of the hatch – the weather, the temperature, when you opened it and when they hatched so that you can learn from it for the future.

✳

47

▲ Breeding pens.

You should also see some red veins at this stage. Eggs that are "clear" need to be discarded. Don't keep the incubator open for too long and candle again about a week later.

Most incubators have an inbuilt hatcher (again check instructions). If this is the case take out the egg rollers, put in the hatching tray a couple of days before hatching is due and keep the lid closed. Pipping (when the hatchling starts to break through the shell) should then begin. It can take up to a day for a duckling to emerge. Do not intervene – especially in the early stages when it would kill the emerging duckling. Leave them in the hatcher for 24 hours to dry (they become fluffy). They will be living on what they have absorbed from the yolk. Then they need transferring to their rearing pen.

You can leave un-hatched eggs a couple more days but candle them to see what is happening. Usually the embryo is dead in the shell – often from a humidity imbalance.

▲ Candle the eggs to check their viability.

▲ Hatching and rearing sheds.

▲ A feeding trough for chicks.

Taking care of ducklings

THE DUCK OR HEN will take care of ducklings she has hatched but she needs safety from predators to do this and they need duckling crumbs for food and access to clean, safe water. Don't provide swimming water until they are at least a few weeks old and make sure they cannot get into her washing water – they can't climb so a high edged tub should stop them. A hen cannot provide the preen oil to make ducklings waterproof so they quite literally will become waterlogged and drown if they get into water until their own preen glands are working – about a month old. (The same thing goes for ducklings hatched with an incubator.) The ducklings will get under the mother for warmth when they need it but if the weather is very cold or wet, then provide a sheltered house and run – maybe even an indoor building if the weather is really rough.

▲ The ducklings will take shelter under their mother if the weather is too cold.

Ducklings without a mother

It is up to you to provide all the conditions that the mother would have done so initially you need to "brood" the baby ducklings – keep them warm together. You can buy ready made brooders but most people use a DIY brooder. This is a round pen constructed from a solid material such as hard board to keep out draughts, with a heat lamp, preferably a dull emitter that doesn't blast them with bright light as well as heat, suspended in the middle. Drinking water and duckling crumbs will be placed to the side of the lamp. Initially you can use a cardboard box but line the corners so ducklings cannot get trapped and be careful about the fire risk. Have soft shavings or chopped straw litter on the floor. The lamp can be raised or lowered according to how much heat is needed. The ducklings do need to be able to get away from the heat. If the ducklings are too hot, they will move away and if too cold, they will huddle under it. Watch them carefully and adjust accordingly.

The brooder must be in a safe place away from domestic animals, mammal and bird predators. As the ducklings grow, raise the lamp, perhaps turning it off on warm days until eventually the heat source is not needed. Gradually introduce the ducklings to an outside run on warm days – bringing them in at night until they can be left out night and day in a predator safe pen. Introduce shallow swimming water when they are over a month old but watch them for any distress or water logging. Your careful observation will help you tell when the ducklings are content and well and give early warning signs for chilled ducklings, sick ones or if they need to move up a stage. They are very messy and do need to be kept very clean. As with adults, they like to have water with their food – and then paddle it round the pen!

What is good health?

BECAUSE YOU WILL GET to know your ducks and how they all behave, you will soon notice if one is behaving differently. This is a good indication of any problems. Every day, cast your eye over your flock and check that they are all:–

~ Eager to come out of the house and head for the feed

~ Their eyes are bright and without a discharge

~ The plumage is clean and shiny
~ Their bottom area (or vent) where excretion passes, should be clean without excreta clinging to it
~ The duck is not lame or limping – also watch out for a duck that cannot walk in a straight line
~ The duck is not bleeding or injured

If a duck is not well, then it will need to be caught and examined – the first thing to do is to feel the weight. It is sometimes hard to see how thin a bird is but you can soon feel it by the weight and whether the breast bone is thin and protruding.

Isolate the bird – if this distresses it you might have to pen it away from, but where it can see, the others. A sick bird must be kept separate, not only because the disease might be contagious (though this is not as likely as other causes), but to stop others trampling on it or a drake trying to mate with it. You can then see how much it is eating and drinking.

Observe for a few hours and if it does not pick up then contact your vet with as much information as you can – does it eat? does it drink? can it stand or walk? This will help the vet to come to the correct diagnosis.

Prevention is better than cure so

꙳Make sure all ducks have access to food and water and are not bullied away by others

꙳Make sure ducks are not harassed by over amorous drakes

꙳Don't mix newly purchased birds with existing birds without careful planning

꙳Make sure ground doesn't contain sharp stones or glass for webbed feet

꙳Make sure your ducks have sufficient area to forage and range

꙳Always keep the duck house and run clean

꙳Make sure ducks cannot eat slug pellets or other chemical substances

꙳Have a regular worming programme

꙳Have an external parasite prevention plan

꙳Supply plenty of clean water for splashing and dipping the head and neck.

▲ Plenty of water for splashing is vital.

▲ Ducks need to forage for food.

✔ Basic health care

THE DUCK'S INTERNAL ORGANS are well adapted to digest food using the grinding action in the gizzard and pass droppings quickly and easily which, in wild ducks, allow them to absorb nutrition yet not put on so much weight they cannot easily get airbourne. It helps to have a basic idea of the internal functions of a duck to fully understand their management.

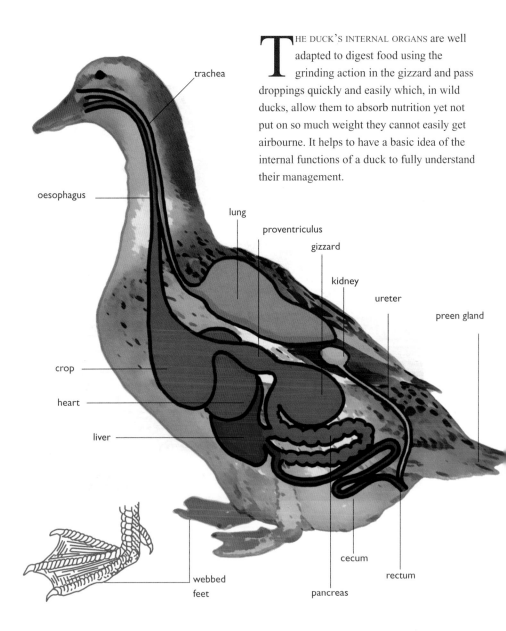

trachea

oesophagus

lung

proventriculus

gizzard

kidney

ureter

preen gland

crop

heart

liver

webbed feet

pancreas

cecum

rectum

▲ How a duck looks from the inside.

Ducks kept correctly are naturally healthy and hardy. It is important that when the end of life comes you are able to provide an instant and painless death, as with any animal. But they should have a good long life of up to ten years or more under normal circumstances.

Parasite prevention

Internal parasites use the bird's body as a host for their life cycle and it is important to use regular worming to keep these in check.

Ducks are prone to Gape worms where the duck stretches its neck and almost gasps as a symptom, Gizzard worms which is where parasites live in the gizzard causing devastating damage and Roundworms that congregate in the digestive system. Consult your vet to decide on a prevention programme – there are now excellent poultry wormers available in sizes that are suitable for a small number of pet ducks.

External parasites are less of a problem in ducks than in chickens (who wants to live on something that keeps immersing its body in water?) but they do become a problem when the numbers of mite are high especially where a house is used year after year as they can live in crevices and come out at night to feed on birds. They become a big problem when a duck goes broody as they quite literally have a sitting duck target. Control them with proprietary sprays and powders applied both to the duck, the bedding and the house (check the label for instructions) and wash out the house at least every year then treat with an anti-mite product. Another nasty mite is Northern Mite which is especially keen on ducks. Fly strike, where a blow fly lays its eggs around the vent of a duck, will produce flesh eating maggots, some of which might go inside and prove fatal. Look out for these in "fluffy" feathered ducks and older ones. Ducks that have access to natural water can also be affected by leeches or ticks which should simply be removed.

▲ Ducks are naturally healthy and hardy.

✦ Common ailments

Breathing problems

These are usually caused either by an infectious disease which will require veterinary intervention but more often by poor ventilation within the duck house, damp bedding causing mould spores, mouldy food and so on. The duck may still need vet treatment but the cause must also be corrected so the problem doesn't reoccur.

Lameness

Even slight lameness can turn into a really difficult problem possibly leading to death. The most common cause is Bumble Foot where the web has been injured probably by treading on a sharp stone. If you can pick up on this quickly and via your vet give antibiotics and keep it clean and open then it won't develop into the swollen web that is Bumble Foot. Once it does,

the treatment is more complicated and not always successful.

Other causes of lameness are muscle strain or even breaks from straining to get in and out of water, over-enthusiastic mating, bullying, fighting or escaping from predators. Isolate and seek veterinary advice. Bad breaks may need immediate euthanasia but some can heal.

Digestive Problems

Any difference to the normal in droppings must be a cause for concern such as really foul smelling, watery droppings and any droppings that contain blood. An enteritis will need immediate veterinary treatment and then the cause such as bad hygiene or infected water, removed.

Crop binding is when food cannot pass down the gizzard and can be blocked by very

▲ Webbed feet are delicate and any injury must be treated.

▶ Ducks are an enthusiastic bunch and this can sometimes cause them to injure themselves.

▲ Ducks must have plenty of water available to drink.

▲ Bread is not good for ducks except in small quantities and mixed with water.

long grass, garden string or plastic or even gizzard worms. Causes are as before but also lack of grit for grinding. Gentle massage may remove impaction but more usually vet intervention to remove the obstruction is necessary.

▲ These ducklings may live up to ten years.

Egg problems

Egg binding is where the bird cannot pass an egg. If it is a "simple" obstruction, in a warm area, smear Vaseline around the vent and gently ease out the egg. If this does not work, then vet advice is needed. Prolapse is where in females part of the oviduct protrudes from the vent, in males where the penis cannot retract. Seek vet advice.

By learning what a duck needs and providing it and by good observation, most vet problems will be avoided and you and your ducks should have many happy years together.

▲ Alway keep an eye on your ducks.

▲ You and your ducks should enjoy many happy years together.

🦆 Glossary

Air sac: (or air space) This is at the broad end of a fertilised egg and expands as the embryo grows. Humidity has an effect on growth.

Albumen: White of egg.

Ark: Moveable triangular strong house usually with a run that can be moved around but is often too small for keeping ducks in all the time.

Avian Flu: Two strains – low pathogenic (LPAI) and highly pathogenic (HPAI). HPAI includes the H5N1 strain of concern to health experts. Both are notifiable and are found worldwide.

Balanced ration: (also known as Compound feeds/ concentrates) Normally found in a bag, these are carefully balanced and mixed by the feed manufacturer for specific times in the duck's life e.g. ducklings, laying and so on.

▲ Bill.

▲ A bantam.

Bantam: A true bantam has no larger version but (the term) is often used to denote a miniature of a breed as well.

Bill: The beak of duck.

Brooder: A purpose built machine for rearing young birds which includes in-built heat.

Broody: When a duck wants to sit on eggs and hatch them off – shown by being very vocal and often unusually aggressive especially if being moved.

Candling: Using strong light to look at the development of the embryo.

Collar: A way to describe a narrow strip of light colour round a duck's neck.

Crest: Feathers on the top of a duck's head – only a few breeds have these.

▲ Domestic ducks.

▲ Ducklings.

Cross bred: The offspring of two different breeds or even of cross breeds themselves.

Domestic ducks: These breeds have been developed for the table or for eggs and to be more docile than wildfowl.

Down: Small, very fluffy feathers under the top feathers which keep the duck warm and, when the duck is dead, can be used to provide stuffing for pillows and quilts.

Drake: A male duck.

Duck: A female duck or a term used to identify the species.

Ducklings: Young ducks – a term usually used while they are still in their downy plumage but sometimes used for a table bird of up to six/seven weeks. Ducklings in down need some sort of heat source if they don't have a mother.

Flights: The large feathers which include the primaries and secondaries – it is the primaries on one side that are trimmed to stop flight and have to be re-trimmed after every moult.

Free range: Ducks that range freely over a large area during the day – still need to be housed at night to protect from predators.

▲ A drake.

▲ Free range ducks.

Gizzard: The organ in the neck that grinds the food – needs grit to work properly.

Hybrids: Planned cross-breds for commercial purposes.

Infra-red: Type of lamp used to provide heat to young ducklings but can also be used for sick birds. Use a dulled lamp not a bright lamp.

Meal: A powdered form of the balanced ration – must be fed wet to ducks. More usually in pellet form (still needs water available while eating).

Moult: The act of losing old feathers and replacing with new. Ducks are often vulnerable during this period as they require good food to make up the new feathers and they cannot fly.

Pin feathers: When feathers emerge after a moult they show through as "pins" until they open out into feathers.

Preening: The act of oiling feathers from the

▲ Preening.

preening gland which is at the base of the tail – water is required for this vital task to be accomplished.

Pure bred: From a specific, recognised breed as standardised in the Poultry Club of Great Britain Standards. (Other countries have similar organisations).

Sex Curls: The curly tail of the drake that indicates he is male.

▶ Sex curls.

Table birds: Breeds that are bred specifically for meat – these are heavy and quickly put on weight.

Trio: Two ducks and a drake.

Utility breed: Bred for meat and eggs and very popular pre, during and post the second World War.

Vent: The rear opening which expels eggs and faeces – the end of the digestive tract and the oviduct.

Wildfowl: Sometimes known as Ornamental – normally more timid than domestic ducks, are not kept for eggs or table and frequently need more specialised care.

✦ Index

Abacot Range 13
agricultural shows 20
air sac 43
albumen 42, 43
arks 26
artificial pool 6
auction sales 22
Australia 14
avian flu 26, 60
Aylesbury duck 16

bad weather 37
balanced diet 32, 60
Bantam 10, 60
bill 6, 13, 16, 60
breathing problems 56
breeder pellets 32
breeding pens 48
broody 36, 44, 60
brooder 51, 60
bullying 37, 38
Bumble Foot 56

Call duck 11
candling 60
chalaza 43
chick crumbs 32
China 18
cholesterol 40
clipping 35
coccidiostat 32
collar 60
crest 60
crop binding 56
cross bred 61

digestive problems 56
"Disco Duck" 9
Donald Duck 9
domestic ducks 61
down 61
drake 7, 19, 23, 36, 61
drinkers 33
duck housing 7, 24, 31
ducklings 51, 61

East Indies 14
eggs 13, 37, 40, 41
electric fences 28
egg candler 47

feeders 33
feeding trough 49
fencing 24, 28
finishing pellets 32
foxes 24, 28, 31
flights 61
fly strike 55
free range 61

gape worms 55
germinal disc 42, 43
gizzard 62
gizzard worms 55, 59
grit 33
grower pellets 32

handling 38
hard standing 25
heavy duck breeds 16
hybrids 62

incubator 43, 44, 46, 48, 50
Indian Runner 14
infra-red 62
island 31

Jemima Puddle-Duck 9

Khaki Campbell 8, 12

lameness 36, 52, 56
layer pellets 32
lettuce 33
light duck breeds 12

Magpie 12
maize 32, 36
Mallard 9, 10, 13, 17, 19
meal 62
membrane 42
Miniature Crested, 41
Miniature Appleyard 10
mink 31
Muscovy duck 9, 19

New Zealand 14
"Nice weather for Ducks" 9
Northern Mite 55

Ornamental Waterfowl
  pellets 32

paddling pool 6, 30
Pekin 9, 16, 18
Penguin duck 18
pet carrier 39
pickling 41

pin feathers 62
pipping 48
pond liners 31
ponds 8, 26, 27, 31
potatoes 33
plumage 52
Poultry Club of Great Britain
  20, 62
preen glands 31, 50
preening 62
prolapse 59
predators 7, 28
primary coverts 35
primary flight feathers 35
private sales 22

rats 36
rearing shed 49
Rouen 17

roundworms 55

salmonella 41
secondary flight feathers 35
sex curls 62
shell membrane 43
shows 20
Silkies 44
Silver Appleyard 8, 11, 18
Silver Appleyard
  Miniature 11
Silver Bantam 11

Teal 9
transporting 38
Tufted duck 9

USA 18
Utility breed 62

vent 52, 59, 62

waterglass 41
webbed feet 54
Welsh Harlequin 13
wheat 32, 36
Wigeon 9
wildfowl 8, 30, 47, 62

yolk membrane 43

ACKNOWLEDGEMENTS
Photographer: Rupert Stephenson
David Chapman, photo page 50
Sue Rose, photos pages 1, 27, 52, 59, 62; artwork pages 35, 43, 54
William Hutchison, Head Greenkeeper, Elfordleigh Hotel and Golf Club,
www.elfordleigh.co.uk, photos pages 32, 34, 37 , 27, 57, 58, 61